Here we are again at
number 3 Tree Street.
What's going to happen today?
Nobody is coming out.

Oh, Bangers and Mash are watching TV.
What's on?
Oh, it's Superchimp.

2

That looks exciting.
Just look at him fly.
I'm afraid that's given them an idea.

They are going to play at Superchimp.
Look at them swing from tree to tree.

4

But it's only pretending.
If only they could fly.
If only they had wings like that bird.

Is it a bird?
No, it's Mrs Snitchnose.
I wonder what dirty work she has been
up to?

This pretending is not much fun.
Perhaps it would be more fun at the pond.
There's something flying.

It's the duck.
And the ducklings are taking off.
Everyone can fly except the chimps.

8

Just a minute, what's that beside
Mrs Snitchnose's door?
Yes, it's her broomstick.

9

Now if Bangers borrowed ...
just borrowed the broomstick ...
they could fly.
Superchimps!

10

But dare he borrow it?
Oh, he has.
Will Mrs Snitchnose find out?

Bangers is jumping up and down
like a kangaroo.
But the broomstick won't take off.

Mash has got up a tree with
the broomstick.
Oh dear, he's crashed into that
prickly bush.

13

Bangers, perhaps if you climbed higher ...
Look out, Gran!

14

Perhaps if Mash rode fast on his bike
the broomstick would take off.
Oh dear, the post will be late today.

What a rotten broomstick!
It won't fly at all.

16

Here comes Dad.
What's this? It's a new broom.
It must be a present from Mum.

I think we had better look in
Mrs Snitchnose's house.
Oh dear, she's awake.

18

What's this?
Who's pinched my broomstick?
Oh dear, the Postchimp is telling her.

That looks like a book of spells.
She's off to number 3.
Having to walk is making her mad.

Oh dear, there's Dad sweeping the path.
I think a spell is coming.

21

What's that looping the loop up there?
Is it Superchimp?

22

No, it's Dad. And he's coming down.
Oh no, he's crashing into the pond.

I don't know about Superchimp...
but I think Bangers and Mash
have been Superchumps.
Don't you?

24